SPOT THE DIFFERENCE
OLD MASTERS
EDITION

imagine THAT!™

Imagine That! is an imprint of Top That! Top That! Publishing Inc.
25031 Avenue Stanford, Suite #60, Valencia, CA 91355
www.topthatpublishing.com
Copyright © 2004 Top That! Publishing plc
2 4 6 8 9 7 5 3 1
Printed and bound in China

Contents

Introduction

Welcome to *Spot the Difference: Old Masters*, an ostensibly irreverent look at the world of high art.

The book can be understood on many levels: it's up to you how you wish to take it.

You may wish to see it simply as a children's game but with the subject matter designed for adults. Perhaps you will feel that adding the dimension of spot the difference is a dig at the pretension that can sometimes be found in the art world, particularly in art criticism.

Alternatively, you may see it as an eloquent introduction to the world of art criticism. By accepting the invitation to spot the differences between the masterpiece and the fake you are forced to study the pictures closely. Thus you are likely to make more observations about the paintings than you otherwise might. You may also find pictures you are not familiar with and these might inspire you to find out more about the artist and his work.

The budding art critic may wish to interpret the invitation to play a child's game with great art a comment on some of the fears that are a part of the zeitgeist: the "dumbing down" of education and the need to find exciting new ways to communicate the message to an audience that might otherwise be uninterested.

The critic might also consider that the book raises questions about the financial value society places on art. An original work by van Gogh sells for millions of dollars and yet an imitation of the same quality will only be worth a fraction of the value. If van Gogh depicts himself with the wrong ear cut off how much does it actually matter?* The quality of the art remains virtually the same.

A word about the title. The phrase "Old Masters" usually refers to the great painters 1500 and 1800 and their works but many of the pictures here were completed post-1800 and, therefore, fall outside the definition. Thus even the title hints at the modern idea that knowledge in itself is unimportant, it is how we respond to the information presented to us that matters.

However you wish to interpret the nature of the book, one thing is clear: the presentation of the works in book form allows them to be studied in peace and close up. The distractions of the art gallery are avoided and the interactivity of the spotting of the differences brings the masterpieces into the modern age.

* Van Gogh cut off his left ear but his famous picture shows the right ear bandaged. This is because he used a mirror for the self-portrait.

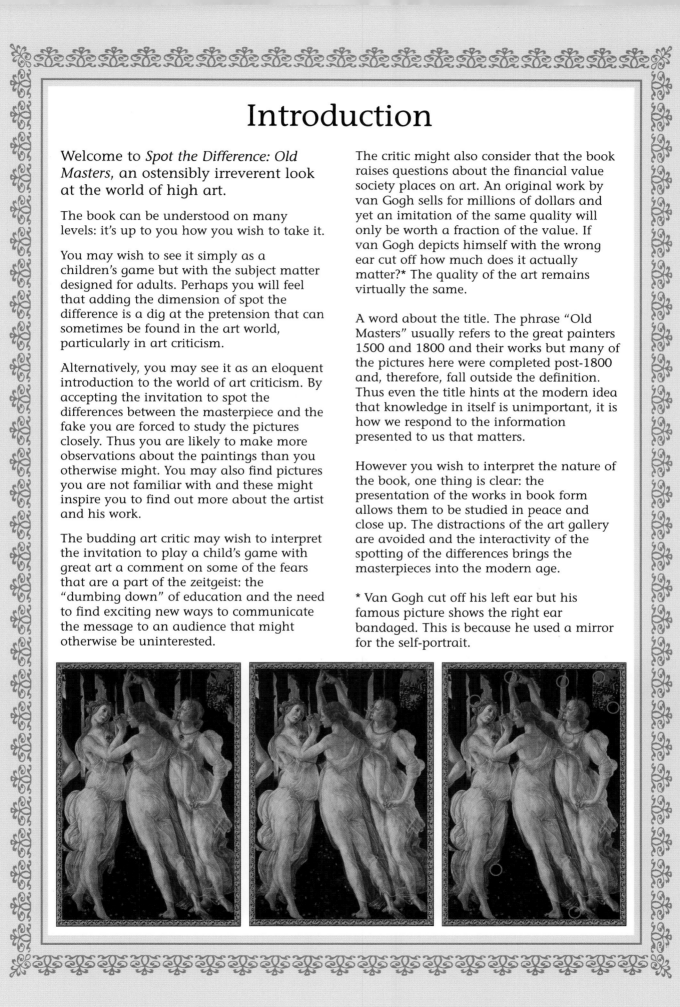

Anubis Concluding Mummification of Dead Man—Unknown

All Ancient Egyptian art was completed for the "ka," the soul after death. Anubis
was the Egyptian god associated with death. He took the form of a jackal, perhaps
because these animals could often be found prowling around tombs.

Dancer Drawing—Degas

Edgar Degas (1834-1917) is one of the best-known French Impressionists.
He specialized in studies of ballet, horse racing, and young women at work.
His style was influenced by Japanese prints and photography.

Young Dancers—Degas

Degas was fascinated by ballet dancers throughout his working life, painting and sculpting them time and time again. Interestingly, he preferred not to pose his subjects but to paint them as they moved.

Fishing Boats on the Beach at Saintes-Maries—van Gogh

Dutch artist Vincent van Gogh (1853-1890) is regarded as a Post-Impressionist. His style is distinguished by intense color and expressive brushwork. Thought of as a genius today, he barely sold a painting in his lifetime.

The Man with his Ear Cut off—van Gogh

When the mentally unstable van Gogh fell into an argument with Paul Gauguin he threatened his fellow artist with a razor. Later, full of remorse for his behavior he cut part of his own ear off with the razor.

Bedroom at Arles—van Gogh

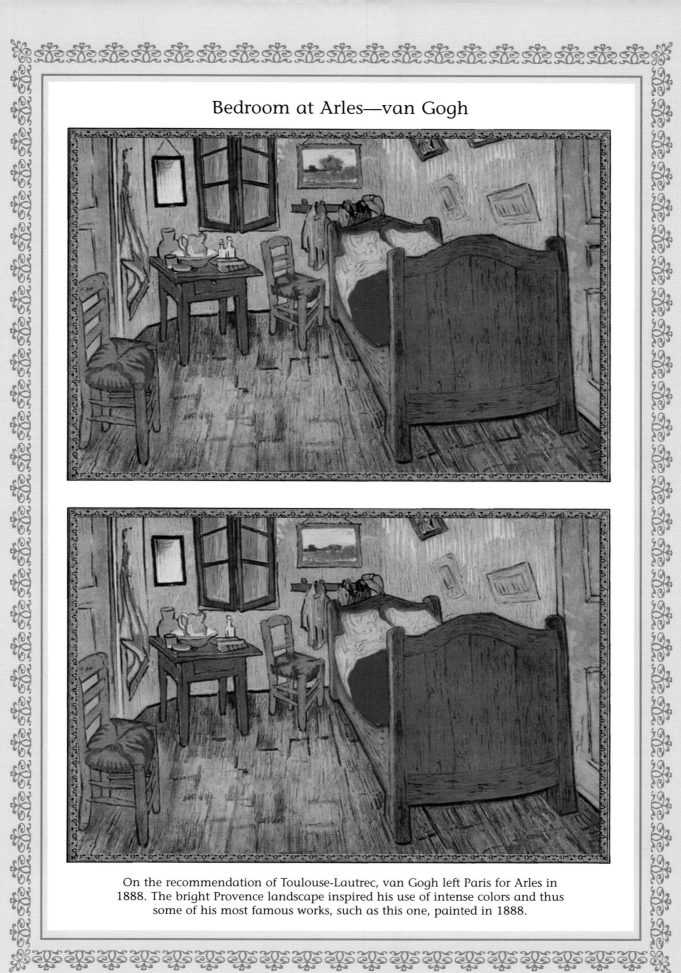

On the recommendation of Toulouse-Lautrec, van Gogh left Paris for Arles in 1888. The bright Provence landscape inspired his use of intense colors and thus some of his most famous works, such as this one, painted in 1888.

Portrait of Dr Gachet—van Gogh

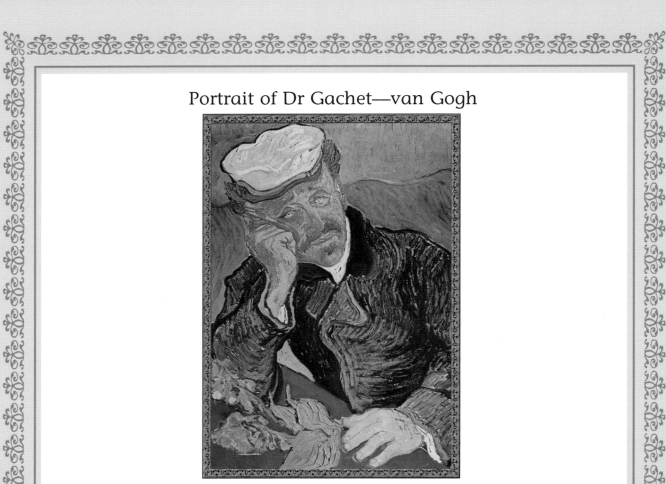

Shortly before his suicide van Gogh lived under the supervision of Dr Gachet, a man who the artist described as "sicker than I am, I think, or shall we say just as much." This portrait of his physician is one of his most famous works.

La Orana Maria—Gauguin

The Post-Impressionist Frenchman Paul Gauguin (1848-1903) moved to Tahiti in 1891. His work is considered important partly because he made primitive art a significant field. As such, he became a huge influence on 20th-century art.

The Fifer—Manet

French painter Edouard Manet (1832-1883) was heavily influenced by Spanish artists
before joining the Impressionists in the 1880s, who came to regard him as a father figure.
His work is distinguished by his use of contrast and the verve of his paint handling.

Luncheon of the Boating Party—Renoir

Another French Impressionist, Pierre-Auguste Renoir (1841-1919) is noted for his lively, colorful painting style and feathery brushwork—known as his "rainbow" style. He specialized in scenes of everyday life and female nudes.

Le Moulin de la Galette—Renoir

The Moulin de la Galette was a place of entertainment in the Montmartre area of Paris. This painting depicts one of the Sunday afternoon dances that took place there and is regarded as one of his happiest compositions.

Madame Charpentier and her Children—Renoir

Painted in the same year as "Moulin de la Galette," at the time Renoir was earning his living from portraiture. It is interesting to note that he was developing the ability to paint joyous shimmering color and flickering light in outdoor scenes at this time.

Une Baignade Asnières—Seurat

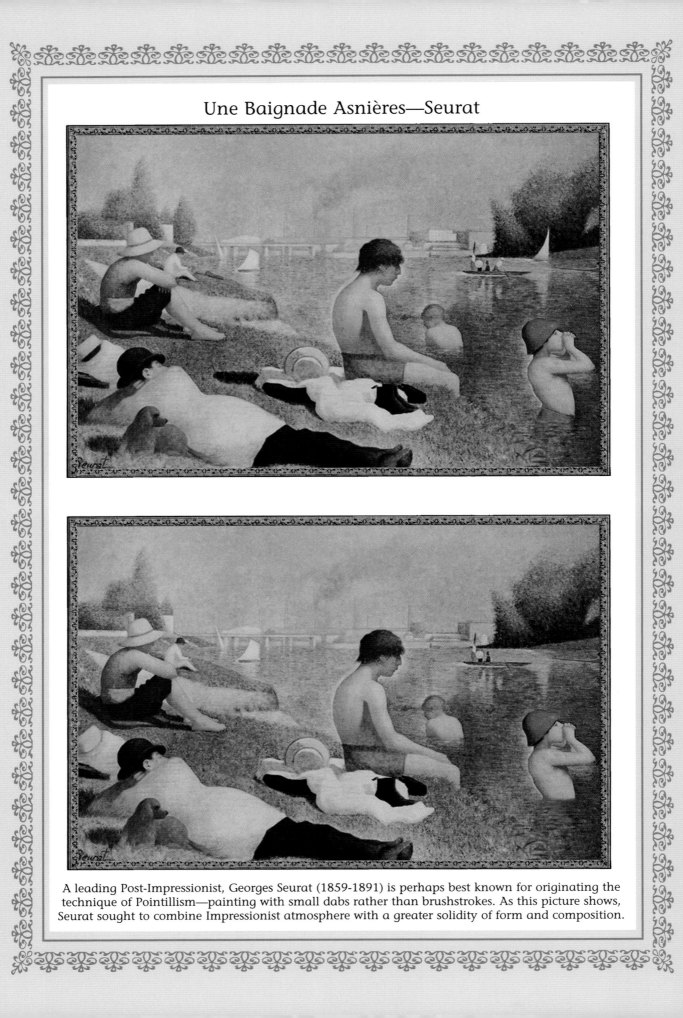

A leading Post-Impressionist, Georges Seurat (1859-1891) is perhaps best known for originating the technique of Pointillism—painting with small dabs rather than brushstrokes. As this picture shows, Seurat sought to combine Impressionist atmosphere with a greater solidity of form and composition.

Field of Poppies—Monet

Claude Monet (1840-1926) was a pioneer of Impressionism and its aims: to depict real life, to paint straight from nature and to capture the changing effects of light. To explore the effects of light he would paint the same subject at different times of day.

Place de L'Europe on a Rainy Day—Caillebotte

The work of the lesser-known Impressionist Gustave Caillebotte (1848-1894) has been neglected until recently. He is best known for the realism of his paintings of Parisian boulevards from a high vantage point.

Hunt near Fontainebleau—Vernet

Carle Vernet (1758-1836) specialized in paintings of horses and military scenes.
He was awarded the Legion of Honor by Napoleon for his depictions
of the battles of Marengo and Austerlitz.

La Goulue and Madame Fromage at the Moulin Rouge—Toulouse-Lautrec

The first child of first cousins, Henri Toulouse-Lautrec (1864-1901) suffered from skeletal deformities and dwarfism. A heavy drinker who probably suffered from syphilis, his work tended to reflect on the darker side of life, as shown by his many studies of prostitutes.

Beata Beatrix—Rossetti

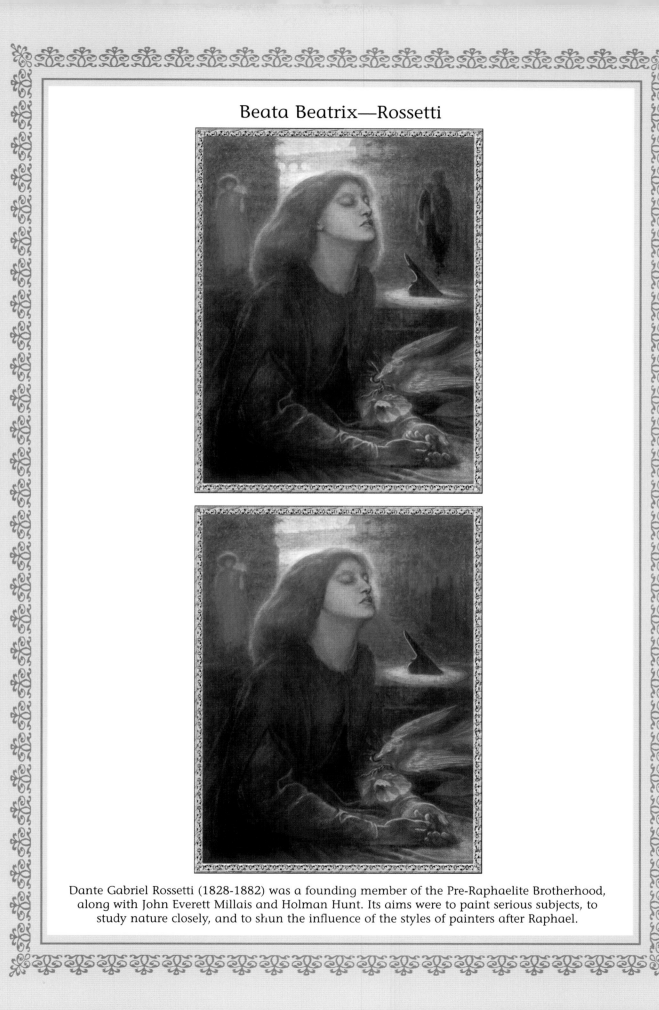

Dante Gabriel Rossetti (1828-1882) was a founding member of the Pre-Raphaelite Brotherhood, along with John Everett Millais and Holman Hunt. Its aims were to paint serious subjects, to study nature closely, and to shun the influence of the styles of painters after Raphael.

La Ghirlandata—Rossetti

"La Ghirlandata" is one of Rossetti's more decorative works. The title of the work comes from the garland on the upper left side of the painting. Composed of roses and honeysuckle blossoms, there is some suggestion that the garland alludes to desire and passion.

The Death of Chatterton—Henry Wallis

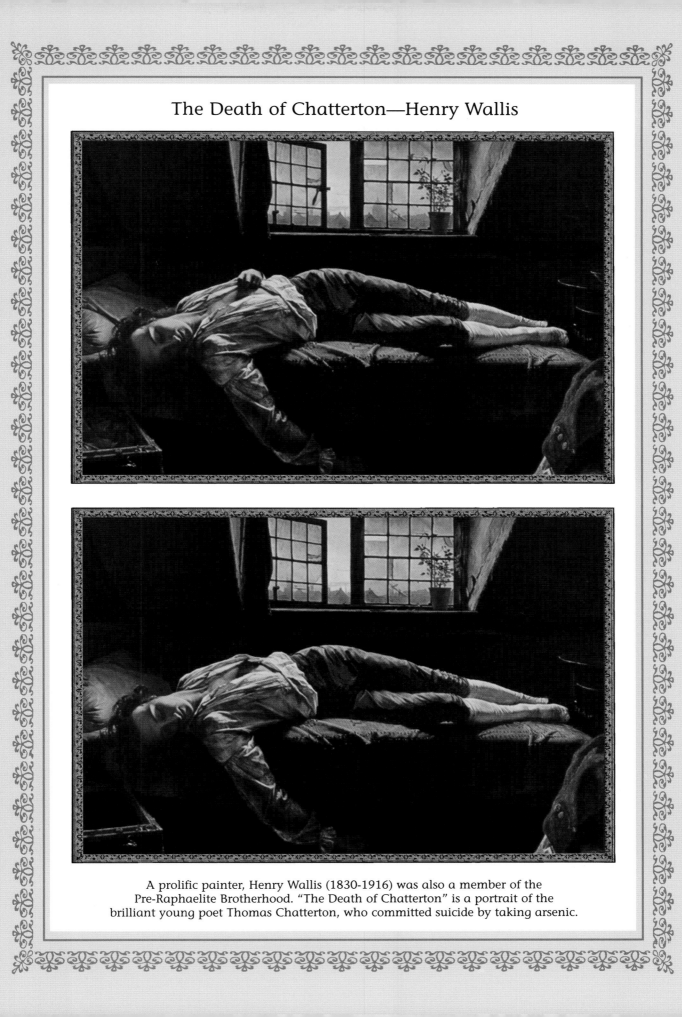

A prolific painter, Henry Wallis (1830-1916) was also a member of the
Pre-Raphaelite Brotherhood. "The Death of Chatterton" is a portrait of the
brilliant young poet Thomas Chatterton, who committed suicide by taking arsenic.

Puss in Boots—Millais

The Pre-Raphaelite Brotherhood proved short-lived and Sir John Everett Millais (1829-1896) developed an academic style of presenting popular sentiment. His colorful portraits of lovers, children, and powerful men proved very popular with Victorian society.

The Blue Boy—Gainsborough

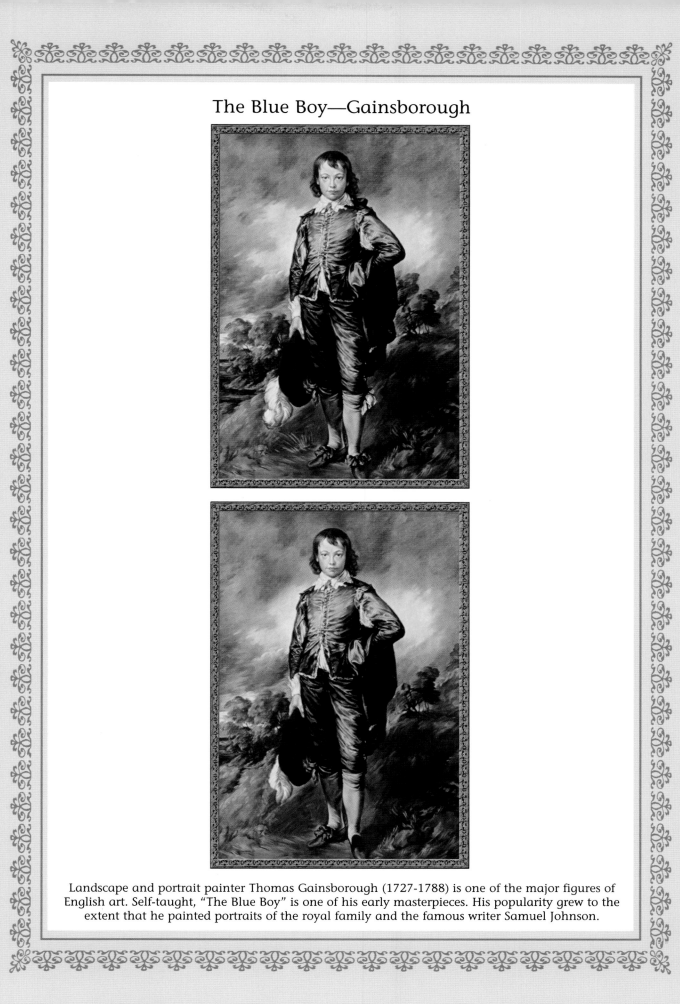

Landscape and portrait painter Thomas Gainsborough (1727-1788) is one of the major figures of English art. Self-taught, "The Blue Boy" is one of his early masterpieces. His popularity grew to the extent that he painted portraits of the royal family and the famous writer Samuel Johnson.

The Haywain—Constable

John Constable (1776-1837) was one of the greatest landscape artists of the 19th century.
His paintings are notable for their atmospheric effects and the eloquence of their expression
of his love for the British countryside. "The Haywain" is his best-known painting.

A Special Pleader—Burton Barber

British artist Charles Burton Barber (1845-1894) specialized in paintings of dogs, cats, and other animals. Barber's work varied from the almost photographic to the sketchy, and tended towards the sentimental.

Golden Hours—Cobbett

Minor British artist Edward John Cobbett (1815-1899) is best remembered for his genre scenes and landscapes. "Golden Hours" is one of his better-known works.

Thoughts of the Past—Spencer Stanhope

Minor British artist John Roddam Spencer Stanhope (1829-1908) was a member of a group of artists who worked on the Oxford Union murals. Some find his use of color too strong and unsubtle and his drawing too harsh.

Testa di Giovinetta—Leonardo da Vinci

Leonardo da Vinci (1452-1519) is the most outstanding figure of the Renaissance. The strength of his work is founded on his patient and searching study of nature and most particularly, light and shade. Not only a gifted artist, his understanding of the sciences was also truly impressive.

Mona Lisa—Leonardo da Vinci

Leonardo's most famous painting, "Mona Lisa" was painted in 1504. Although the true identity of the subject is unknown many experts believe it to be the wife of a Florentine businessman, Francesco del Giocondo.

Birth of Venus—Botticelli

Although Florentine artist Sandro Botticelli (1445-1510) produced mostly religious works, he is best known for his treatments of mythological subjects. By the time of his death his linear style was out of fashion but it proved a source of inspiration for the Pre-Raphaelites.

Venezia, Santa Maria della Salute—Canaletto

Canaletto is the adopted name of Italian artist Giovanni Antonio Canal (1697-1768). He painted highly detailed views of his native Venice and of London and the river Thames. He proved to be very influential on British painters such as William Hogarth and Richard Wilson.

Venice, The Square of Saint Mark—Canaletto

Thanks to artists such as Titian and Tintoretto, the Renaissance is regarded as the high point of Venetian art. Artists such as Canaletto and Tiepolo helped to maintain Venice's reputation for high art into the 18th century even though their work is now commonly regarded as inferior to their predecessors.

Tipos Populares Espanoles—Tiepolo

Lorenzo Tiepolo (1736-1776) was the son of the more famous Italian artist Giambattista Tiepolo. In 1750 he traveled with his father to Würzburg to assist him with some decorative frescoes. A number of drawings from this time have now been attributed to him.

Le Printemps—Arcimboldo

Italian artist Giuseppe Arcimboldo (1527-1593) began his career as a designer of stained-glass windows for Milan cathedral. His fantastic heads composed of non-human details influenced the surrealists of the 20th century, such as Salvador Dali.

Paesaggio con Pescatori—Grimaldi

An eclectic artist of the Bolognese school, Giovanni Francesco Grimaldi (1606-1680) was once employed by Pope Innocent X to paint frescoes in the Vatican. His main pictures are at the Colonna in Rome and galleries in Vienna.

Flemish Fair—Brueghel the Younger

The son of distinguished Dutch artist Pieter Brueghel the Elder, Pieter Brueghel the Younger (1564-1638) was sometimes known as "Hell" because of his paintings of diabolical scenes with devils, hags, or robbers.

A Man in Armor—Rembrandt

Rembrandt Harmensz van Rijn (1606-1669) is regarded as the greatest northern European artist of his age. His work is distinguished by its technical mastery, sense of drama, and sense of humanity. He produced over 600 paintings in the course of his lifetime.

The Four Elements: Water—Jan Brueghel

The youngest son of Pieter Brueghel the Elder, Jan Brueghel the Elder (1568-1625)
painted still life, flowers, landscapes, and religious subjects, usually on a
small scale.

Dutch artist Abraham van Beyeren (1620-1690) is another artist who only really achieved recognition posthumously. Now considered one of the greatest still-life painters, he started painting fish before focusing on expensive table coverings.

The Lace Maker—Vermeer

An art dealer, Dutch artist Jan Vermeer (1632-1675) made little effort to sell his paintings during his lifetime. His paintings, usually detailed studies of domestic interiors, were not considered significant until the late 19th century.

Kuchenmagd—Vermeer

Vermeer was able to achieve a great sense of realism in his paintings because of his understanding of visual perception. This can be seen through his subtle use of contrast between objects which are clearly defined and those which are slightly out of focus.

The Laughing Cavalier—Hals

By painting directly onto canvas, Dutch artist Franz Hals (1580-1666) was able to create portraits that seem spontaneous and full of life. Although he was a popular artist of his day he was often threatened by poverty due to his chaotic domestic life.

The Kiss—Klimt

Austrian artist Gustav Klimt (1862-1918) produced a large number of portraits of women as well as large allegorical and mythological paintings. His depictions of women as seductive and dangerous is typical of the decadence associated with the end of the 19th century.

Le Retour de l'Enfant Prodigue—Teniers the Younger

Dutch artist David Teniers the Younger (1610-1690) was the son-in-law of Jan Brueghel. His work was very popular throughout the 18th century and royal houses throughout Europe were keen buyers.

Banker's Table—Harnett

Born in Ireland, William Harnett (1848-1892) emigrated to Philadelphia with his parents where he trained as a silver engraver. He became a painter of trompe l'oeil still lifes in which he depicted common objects in great detail and with photographic realism.

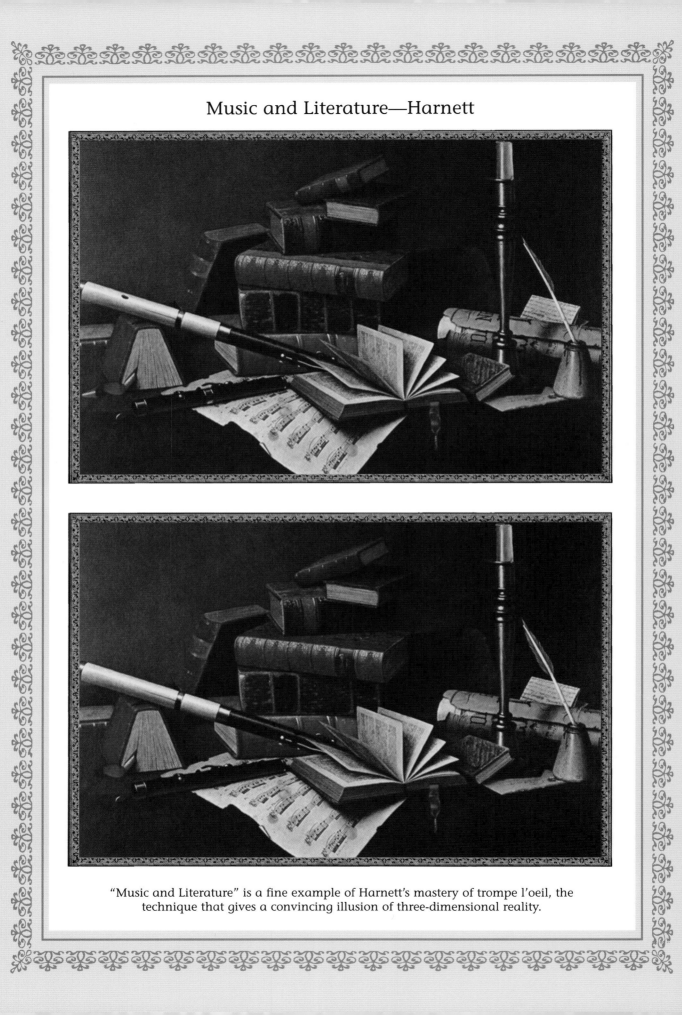

"Music and Literature" is a fine example of Harnett's mastery of trompe l'oeil, the technique that gives a convincing illusion of three-dimensional reality.

Crossing the Stream—Melrose

Born in Scotland, Andrew Melrose (1836-1901) emigrated to the United States around 1855. His atmospheric landscape paintings were inspired by his travels throughout Europe and the Americas.

49

The Smoke Signal—Remington

Frederic Remington (1861-1909) traveled through the American West working as a prospector and cowboy, sketching constantly. He is best known for his paintings and sculptures of cowboys and Native Americans.

Okitsu—Hiroshige

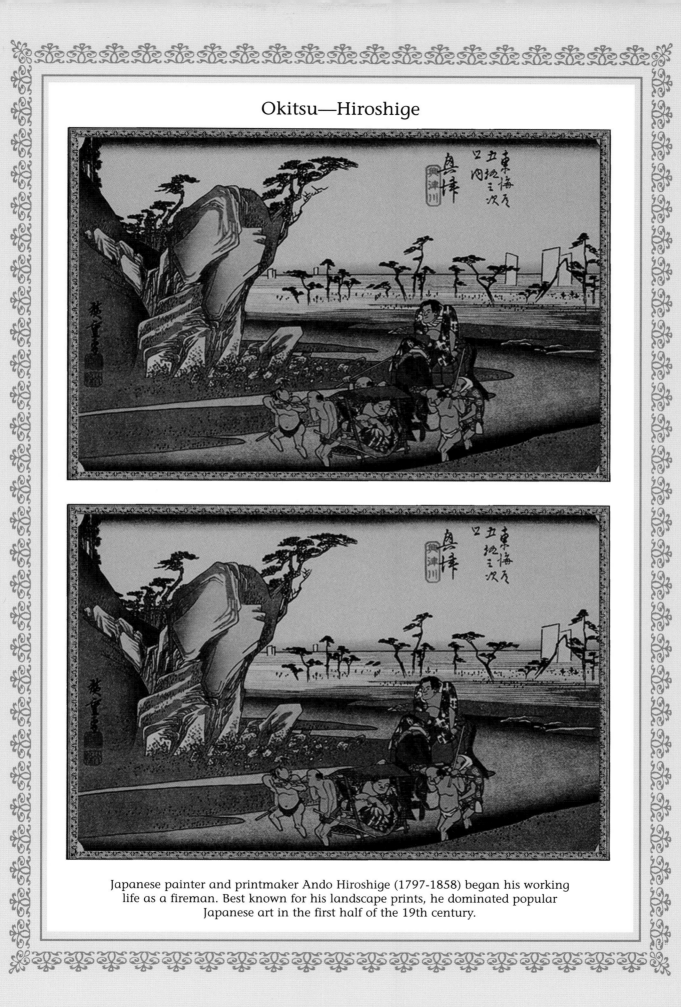

Japanese painter and printmaker Ando Hiroshige (1797-1858) began his working life as a fireman. Best known for his landscape prints, he dominated popular Japanese art in the first half of the 19th century.

Plums, Still Life—Melendez

Although he spent most of his life in poverty, Luis Melendez (1716-1780)
is regarded as the finest Spanish still-life artist of his day. His work is rarely
found outside Spain.

Answers

Page 4 Anubis Concluding Mummification of Dead Man—Unknown

Page 5 Dancer Drawing—Degas

Page 6 Young Dancers—Degas

Page 8 The Man with his Ear Cut off—van Gogh

Page 7 Fishing Boats on the Beach at Saintes-Maries—van Gogh

53

Answers

Page 9 Bedroom at Arles—van Gogh

Page 10 Portrait of Dr Gachet—van Gogh

Page 11 La Orana Maria—Gauguin

Page 12 The Fifer—Manet

Answers

Page 13 Luncheon of the Boating Party—Renoir

Page 14 Le Moulin de la Galette—Renoir

Page 15 Madame Charpentier and her Children—Renoir

Page 16 Une Baignade Asnières—Seurat

Answers

Page 17 Field of Poppies—Monet

Page 18 Place de L'Europe on a Rainy Day—Caillebotte

Page 19 Hunt near Fontainebleau—Vernet

Page 20 La Goulue and Madame Fromage at the Moulin Rouge—Toulouse-Lautrec

Answers

Page 21 Beata Beatrix—Rossetti

Page 22 La Ghirlandata—Rossetti

Page 23 The Death of Chatterton—Henry Wallis

Page 24 Puss in Boots—Millais

Answers

Page 25 The Blue Boy—Gainsborough

Page 26 The Haywain—Constable

Page 27 A Special Pleader—Burton Barber

Page 28 Golden Hours—Cobbett

Answers

Page 29 Thoughts of the Past—
Spencer Stanhope

Page 30 Testa di Giovinetta—Leonardo
da Vinci

Page 31 Mona Lisa—Leonardo da Vinci

Page 32 Birth of Venus—Botticelli

Answers

Page 33 Venezia, Santa Maria delle Salute—Canaletto

Page 34 Venice, The Square of Saint Mark—Canaletto

Page 35 Tipos Populares Espanoles—Tiepolo

Page 36 Le Printemps—Arcimboldo

60

Answers

Page 37 Paesaggio con Pescatori—Grimaldi

Page 38 Flemish Fair—Brueghel the Younger

Page 39 A Man in Armor—Rembrandt

Page 40 The Four Elements: Water—Jan Brueghel

Answers

Page 41 Still Life—van Beyeren

Page 42 The Lace Maker—Vermeer

Page 43 Kuchenmagd—Vermeer

Page 44 The Laughing Cavalier—Hals

Answers

Page 45 The Kiss—Klimt

Page 46 Le Retour de l'Enfant Prodigue—Teniers the Younger

Page 47 Banker's Table—Harnett

Page 48 Music and Literature—Harnett

Answers

Page 49 – Crossing the Stream—Melrose

Page 50 – The Smoke Signal—Remington

Page 51 – Okitsu—Hiroshige

Page 52 – Plums, Still Life—Melendez